Pillow Talk

Trivia for Couples

The Sexy Game of Naughty Trivia Questions

J.R. James

Copyright © 2020 Love & Desire Press

Written by J.R. James

All rights reserved.

ISBN 978-1-952328-43-5 (paperback)

Spice up your love life even more, and explore all the discussion books for couples by J.R. James:

Love and Relationship Books for Couples

Would You Rather...? The Romantic Conversation Game for Couples (Love and Romance Edition)

Sexy Game Books for Couples

Would You Rather...? The Naughty Conversation Game for Couples (Hot and Sexy Edition)

Truth or Dare? The Sexy Game of Naughty Choices (Hot and Wild Edition)

Never Have I Ever... An Exciting and Sexy Game for Adults (Hot and Dirty Edition)

The Hot or Not Quiz for Couples: The Sexy Game of Naughty Questions and Revealing Answers

Pillow Talk: The Sexy Game of Naughty Trivia Questions for Couples

The Naughty Newlywed Game: A Sexy Game of Questions for Couples

Sexy Discussion Books for Couples

Let's Talk Sexy: Essential Conversation Starters to Explore Your Lover's Secret Desires and Transform Your Sex Life

All **THREE** *Let's Talk About...* sexy question books in one massive volume for one low price. Save now!

Let's Talk About... Sexual Fantasies and Desires: Questions and Conversation Starters for Couples Exploring Their Sexual Interests

Let's Talk About... Non-Monogamy: Questions and Conversation Starters for Couples Exploring Open Relationships, Swinging, or Polyamory

Let's Talk About... Kinks and Fetishes: Questions and Conversation Starters for Couples Exploring Their Sexual Wild Side

Change your sex life forever through the power of sexy fun with your spouse, partner, or lover!

www.sexygamesforcouples.com

Sexy Vacations for Couples
https://geni.us/Passion

HOW TO PLAY THE GAME

The rules for this game are very simple:

There needs to be at least two people to play. It's a great game for couples to test their general knowledge about sex, and to test how well they know their partner.

There are two types of questions in this book. The first kind of question is a general trivia question about a sexual topic. The other kind of question is specific to your partner, and tests what you know about their sexuality. You and your partner can either go through the book taking turns asking one another the questions, or you can play the game explained below:

One player reads the question and the multiple choice answers to the other player. The other player guesses the correct answer. Take turns going back and forth asking and answering the trivia questions.

At the end of the round, there will be a *"How well do you know your partner?"* question. Whoever's turn it is to answer a question has the chance to win a sexy reward from the player reading the question.

For example: John and Stephanie are playing together. It's Stephanie's turn to be asked a question so John reads, "Where on my body do I like to be kissed?" Stephanie knows John likes his chest to be kissed, so that's what she guesses his answer would be. John agrees that's his favorite spot, so Stephanie gets to receive the "reward" that's listed under the question from John. John also gets a chance to answer the same question about Stephanie. If he answers correctly, then Stephanie will give John the same reward. Both players get a chance to win! After the sexy rewards are completed, start a new round.

As you spend time discussing the answers, you'll soon you'll find yourselves smiling, laughing, and enjoying the sexually charged conversation. Who knows? You may even discover new sexual possibilities for your relationship.

Just have fun, because as long as you're enjoying time with your partner and sexy conversation, you both win!

NOTE: *Answers to the trivia questions are located in the back of the book beginning on page 90.*

ROUND

1

1

How many times a year does the average American couple have sex?

- a)   32
- b)   66
- c)   89
- d)   126

2

What's the average length of an erect penis?

- a)   4 to 5 inches
- b)   5 to 6 inches
- c)   6 to 7 inches
- d)   8 to 9 inches

3
Which of the following is true about women's sex drives?

a) Women are more influenced by the attitudes of their peer group in decisions abouts sex

b) Women are more likely to call themselves "bisexual"

c) A woman's willingness to perform various sexual practices is more likely to change over time

d) All of the above

4
Which gender has a higher preference for reaching orgasm through oral sex?

a)   Men
b)   Women

5
How long is it before the average man ejaculates during sexual intercourse?

a)   5.4 minutes
b)   8.2 minutes
c)   15.7 minutes
d)   2.3 minutes

6

Stress can make a man's penis shrink.

    a)   True
    b)   False

7

Older women are more likely to experience orgasm when sex is within the context of a relationship.

    a)   True
    b)   False

8

Masturbation can:

a) Improve sexual function
b) Cause genital injury
c) Be a sign of sexual dysfunction
d) All of the above

9

Most women under age 60 think about sex less than once a day.

a) True
b) False

10

What percentage of women say they always have an orgasm during sex with their partner?

a)   13%
b)   29%
c)   38%
d)   72%

11

Most women can have an orgasm without direct stimulation of the clitoris.

a)   True
b)   False

12

What percentage of men say they always have an orgasm during sex with their partner?

a)   31%
b)   58%
c)   75%
d)   96%

13

What's the average number of sexual partners a woman will have in her lifetime?

a)   3.5
b)   8
c)   13
d)   7.5

How well do you know your partner?

Where on my body is my favorite place to be kissed?

Sexy Prize: If your partner can correctly name your favorite area(s), then you must give them a sexy massage for 3 minutes.

ROUND

2

14

The G-spot is a sexually sensitive part of a woman's anatomy and is also known as the clitoris.

    a)   True
    b)   False

15

Sexual activity can increase the risk of stroke and heart attack in older people.

    a)   True
    b)   False

16
What's the average lifetime number of sexual partners for a man?

- a) 7
- b) 4.5
- c) 9
- d) 12

17
What percentage of women can reach orgasm through intercourse alone?

- a) 60%
- b) 90%
- c) 25%
- d) 45%

18

What percentage of women never orgasm at all?

a)   40–45%
b)   10–15%
c)   20–30%
d)   5–10%

19

How many nerve endings does the clitoris have?

a)   8,000
b)   2,500
c)   90
d)   10,000

20

According to a national Kinsey Institute survey, Group Sex (threesomes, orgies, etc.) is the most popular sexual fantasy in the United States.

a) True
b) False

21

How many nerve endings are found in the head of the penis?

a) 40,000
b) 8,000
c) 4,000
d) 300

22

According to the results of a survey conducted by an international condom manufacturer, which country has the most sexual interactions per person per year?

a) United States
b) France
c) Russia
d) Spain
e) Norway
f) Greece

23

How fast do sperm swim?

a)   2 miles per hour
b)   1.5 yards per hour
c)   9 inches per hour
d)   1/8 inch per hour

24

In 1983, what was given out for free to celebrate the king of Thailand's birthday?

a)   Condoms
b)   Prostitutes
c)   Vasectomies
d)   Body shots

25
What was the world's first animated film to receive an X rating?

a) Mickey's Pleasure Cruise
b) The Bunny's Bedroom
c) Monkey Time
d) Fritz the Cat

26
What percentage of men claim to regularly shave their pubic hair?

a) 10%
b) 29%
c) 52%
d) 67%

How well do you know your partner?

What is my favorite sex position?

Sexy Prize: If your partner can correctly name your favorite sex position then you must give them a sexy strip tease and lap dance.

ROUND

3

27

What is the age of the oldest dildo ever discovered?

a)   180 years old
b)   500 years old
c)   28,000 years old
d)   43,000 years old

28

According to statistics, wealthy, educated women are more likely to engage in anal sex.

a)   True
b)   False

29
What percentage of women report having an orgasm during anal sex?

a)   94%
b)   33%
c)   4%
d)   56%

30
How many sexual positions are listed in the Kama Sutra?

a)   64
b)   100
c)   245
d)   83

31

What is the most common injury attributed to sex acts?

a) Bruising
b) Rug burns
c) Bites
d) Pulled muscles

32

Hickeys can cause strokes and have even been documented as a cause of death.

a) True
b) False

33

What percentage of people have reportedly died during sex?

- a) 2.9%
- b) 0.06%
- c) 0.01%
- d) 1.2%

34

It is possible to break a man's penis. Which position is most likely to break it?

- a) Doggy style
- b) Woman on top
- c) Missionary
- d) 69

35
Why were "pubic wigs" worn in the Victorian era?

    a)   To conceal the genitals during sex

    b)   To hide diseases like syphilis

    c)   To prevent transmission of bugs like lice

    d)   It was the style

36
Humans are the only animals who have sex for pleasure, outside of normal reproductive cycles?

    a)   True
    b)   False

37
Sex can help cure a headache.

    a)   True
    b)   False

38
What are the benefits of semen?

    a)   Acts as an antidepressant
    b)   Lowers blood pressure
    c)   Good for the skin
    d)   All of the above

How well do you know your partner?

What is one kink or fetish I'd like to try?

Sexy Prize: If your partner can correctly name one kink or fetish that intrigues you, then you must seductively shower them with soft kisses anywhere they choose for 1 minute.

ROUND

4

39
Where did the term "blow job" come from?

a)   From a man named John Blow who always requested oral sex from the local London prostitutes

b)   From a jazz musician who said it was like blowing a horn

c)   A merging of the Victorian slang for a prostitute (Blowsy) and ejaculation (Blow)

d)   When women used to visit men's colleges, many would sign in under the fake name "Jane Blow"

40

Besides humans, which animal engages in prostitution?

    a)   Penguins
    b)   Lions
    c)   Dolphins
    d)   None

41

You could lose three pounds a year by having sex seven to eight times per month.

    a)   True
    b)   False

42
Watching what type of porn can actually increase a man's chance of impregnating a woman?

a) Heterosexual sex

b) Lesbian sex

c) A threesome with two men and one woman

d) A threesome with two women and one man

43
Early condoms were made of everything but what?

a) Snakeskin
b) Animal intestines
c) Linen soaked in chemicals
d) Animal horns

44
Pubic hair will only grow to a certain length?

a) True
b) False

45
What percentage of men regularly experience premature ejaculation?

a) 5-10%
b) 20-30%
c) 50-65%
d) 75-80%

<u>46</u>

What does the pudendal nerve do?

a)   It transmits information from the uterus in women and the prostate in men to the brain

b)   It transmits information from the clitoris in women and from the scrotum and penis in men to the brain

c)   It transmits information from the vagina in women and the rectum in both sexes to the brain

47

What does "penis captivus" mean?

a)   It's when two people get stuck together during sex

b)   It's the name for a penis that has an unusual, bent shape when fully erect

c)   It is the rare ability to move the penis in a circular motion by flexing muscles

d)   It's when a man's erect penis won't return to its flaccid state

48

What percentage of men worldwide are circumcised?

- a) 20%
- b) 30%
- c) 60%
- d) 80%

49

Someone who is "anorgasmic" is what?

- a) Able to have an orgasm that lasts longer than one minute

- b) Able to have multiple orgasms in a row

- c) Unable to reach orgasm

- d) Unable to have an orgasm lasting longer than 3 seconds

50

If a man wants to avoid erectile dysfunction in the bedroom, what should he lower?

a) The amount of red meat consumed

b) His cholesterol

c) His caloric intake

d) Time spent in the shower

51

Having sex for an hour burns as many calories as which of the following?

a) Swimming for 45 minutes
b) Biking for 10 miles
c) Running a 5-minute mile
d) Jogging for 30 minutes

How well do you know your partner?

What are three things I find extremely sexy?

Sexy Prize: If your partner can correctly name what you find sexy, then you must give them a foot massage for 2 minutes while telling a dirty story.

ROUND

5

52
Where is a man's G-spot located?

a) On the head of the penis
b) On his testicles
c) In his urethra
d) On his prostate gland

53
Ancient Greek women would expose their vaginas to ward off what?

a) Evil
b) Spirits
c) Storms
d) Plague

54
Approximately how many people globally are having sex each day?

    a)   5 million
    b)   3 million
    c)   200 million
    d)   1 billion

55
What well known entertainer insured her boobs for $600,000?

    a)   Pamela Anderson
    b)   Dolly Parton
    c)   Christina Hendricks
    d)   Katie Perry

56

What female part of the anatomy shares its name with the Greek God of Marriage Ceremonies?

   a)   The hymen
   b)   The clitoris
   c)   The uterus
   d)   The vagina

57

Which Great Lakes state has a law making it illegal for a man to shoot a firearm while his female partner has an orgasm?

   a)   Illinois
   b)   Michigan
   c)   Wisconsin
   d)   Minnesota

58

What percentage of people like dirty talk during sex?

a) 22%
b) 58%
c) 81%
d) 13%

59

What other body part routinely swells during sex besides the breasts and genitals?

a) Feet
b) Lips
c) Nose
d) Hands

60

What do Socrates, Aristotle, and Janis Joplin all have in common?

a)   They were bisexual
b)   They were homosexual
c)   They were asexual
d)   They were transsexual

61

In which state is it illegal to have sex without a condom?

a)   Oklahoma
b)   Nevada
c)   Texas
d)   Utah

62
What is the most common fetish in Western society?

a) Spanking
b) Bondage
c) Food
d) Feet

63
Outside of the bedroom, what is the most popular place for Americans to have sex?

a) Shower
b) Kitchen
c) Car
d) Work

How well do you know your partner?

What can you tell me about my first sexual experience?

Sexy Prize: If your partner can give you a reasonably detailed account of your first experience, then you must lick a food item of their choice (whipped cream, chocolate sauce, etc.) off their body.

ROUND

6

64
What food item do scientists believe can cause a stronger arousal than foreplay?

- a) Strawberries
- b) Oysters
- c) Bacon
- d) Chocolate

65
What indie movie featured actress Chole Sevigny giving a real blowjob on camera to the director?

- a) Guns and Rails
- b) Only Cry Once
- c) The Brown Bunny
- d) Easy Rider

66
When was the Kama Sutra written?

a) 4th Century
b) 6th Century
c) 3rd Century
d) 7th Century

67
What is the best position to induce a female orgasm?

a) Reverse cowgirl
b) Missionary
c) Doggy style
d) Woman on top

68
Men can have multiple orgasms.

    a)   True
    b)   False

69
The French call orgasms "la petite mort," which means...

    a)   A good thing
    b)   The little death
    c)   The breath
    d)   The lover's ache

<u>70</u>
What is the "orgasm gap?"

a)   The difference in orgasm frequency between men and women

b)   Time in between orgasms

c)   The difference in male and female orgasm muscle contractions

d)   The amount of time it takes for the brain to send the orgasm signal to the genitals

71
Single women orgasm more than women in relationships.

    a)   True
    b)   False

72
In what country is it illegal for virgins to marry?

    a)   Turkey
    b)   Guam
    c)   Bahrain
    d)   Bolivia

73
For men who are right-handed, which testicle will typically hang lower on your body?

a)   Left testicle
b)   Right testicle

74
After vibrators and fingers, what is the third most popular object used for female masturbation?

a)   Cucumber
b)   Beer bottle
c)   Banana
d)   Candle

75
Orgasms do not lower a women's risk for stroke and breast cancer.

    a)   True
    b)   False

76
What percentage of men have a penis longer than 8 inches?

    a)   15%
    b)   46%
    c)   9%
    d)   3%

How well do you know your partner?

What's my idea of a super sexy night out?

Sexy Prize: If your partner can give a reasonably close description of your ideal erotic evening, then in your best seductive voice, tell them all the ways they're amazing in bed while you nibble their ear. (If you don't know how they are in bed, then make it up.)

ROUND

7

77

According to a global survey conducted by an international condom manufacturer, what is the average amount of time, per week, people spend having sex?

    a)   12 minutes
    b)   35 minutes
    c)   58 minutes
    d)   71 minutes

78
Which country carries a death penalty for masturbating?

a) China
b) Singapore
c) Indonesia
d) Bolivia

79
What percentage of women have admitted to having sex in order to get their guy to do more around the house?

a) 9%
b) 84%
c) 27%
d) 56%

80
Which age group has the lowest rate
of condom usage?

a) Teenagers
b) 20 – 29 years old
c) 30 – 39 years old
d) Over 40 years old

81
According to survey data, which three
countries are recognized for having
the best lovers?

a) Spain, Brazil, and Italy
b) Australia, Peru, and Sweden
c) Argentina, Canada, and India
d) Portugal, Greece, and France

82
What is the world's fourth most popular type of porn?

    a)   Spanking / BDSM
    b)   Transgendered
    c)   Partner swapping
    d)   Girl on girl

83
Straight women have more orgasms on average than lesbian women.

    a)   True
    b)   False

84

What type of female mammal can die if she goes longer than a year without having sex?

  a)   Chimpanzee
  b)   Whale
  c)   Ferret
  d)   Moose

85

Women in ovulation are more likely to cheat.

  a)   True
  b)   False

86

In which state is it illegal to sell sex toys?

a) Texas
b) Alaska
c) Rhode Island
d) Alabama

87

Can being an overweight male contribute to lasting longer in bed?

a) Yes
b) No

88
How many calories are in a teaspoon of semen?

a)   0 calories
b)   5-7 calories
c)   16-18 calories
d)   35-40 calories

89
The world's largest penis on record is how long when fully erect?

a)   9.7 inches
b)   11 inches
c)   13.5 inches
d)   22 inches

How well do you know your partner?

What is something I'd never do in bed?

Sexy Prize: If your partner can correctly name your taboo, then use your tongue to tease them anywhere on their body for 2 minutes.

ROUND

8

90

What percentage of women have reported experiencing an orgasm while exercising?

a) 5%
b) 15%
c) 35%
d) 55%

91

"Formicophilia" is being sexually aroused by what?

a) Puppets
b) Smearing food on one's self
c) Foul odors
d) Crawling insects or worms

92

In 2004, porn star, Lisa Sparxx, set a world record by having sex with how many men in 24 hours?

a)   919 men
b)   112 men
c)   1,511 men
d)   462 men

93

According to a 2019 U.S. survey conducted by TENGA, what male celebrity was the favorite for people to fantasize about while masturbating?

a)   Blake Lively
b)   Jason Momoa
c)   Donald Trump
d)   Paul Ryan

94

From the same 2019 survey found in the previous question, which female celebrity were people most fond of thinking about while masturbating?

a) Jennifer Aniston
b) Kristen Bell
c) Alexis Ford
d) Sophia Vergara

95

Besides humans, which of these animals has also been known to engage in oral sex?

a) Snakes
b) Rabbits
c) Bats
d) Mice

96

Ancient Egyptians applied which of these items to the vagina as a contraceptive?

a) Honey and wine
b) Cat vomit and beer
c) Olive oil and goat's blood
d) Crocodile feces and sour milk

97

A large scale sexual study found what percentage of people over the age of 80 still enjoyed sex regularly?

a) 10%
b) 60%
c) 30%
d) 5%

98
The Kinsey Institute reports at what age does the average female lose her virginity?

a)   17.4 years old
b)   16.1 years old
c)   18.3 years old
d)   20.1 years old

99
Doing more of what has been shown to improve a person's sex life and increase their sexual satisfaction?

a)   Drinking water
b)   Sexual communication
c)   Jogging
d)   Eating vegetables

100
"Sexsomnia" is a real condition that occurs in people who engage in sexual behavior in their sleep.

a) True
b) False

101
Who dreams about sex more, women or men?

a) Women
b) Men

How well do you know your partner?

What parts of someone's body turn me on the most?

Sexy Prize: If your partner can correctly name which parts of the body you find the sexiest, then have them undress, lie down, and lightly caress their body all over using just your fingertips for 3 minutes.

ROUND

9

102

Really, really amazing sex can induce what in some people?

a) Severe itching
b) Temporary amnesia
c) Blindness
d) Uncontrolled sneezing

103

Studies show that people who are poor report greater sexual satisfaction in their lives than their wealthier counterparts.

a) Truc
b) False

<u>104</u>

Which sport can put a man at risk for impotence?

- a) Baseball
- b) Tennis
- c) Golf
- d) Bicycling

<u>105</u>

Male testosterone levels and sperm counts are only a quarter of what they were a century ago.

- a) True
- b) False

106
In Europe, 10% of babies are conceived...

a) Out of wedlock
b) On Christmas day
c) Intentionally
d) On an IKEA bed

107
In what country do men have the largest penises on average?

a) Algeria
b) Congo
c) Ethiopia
d) Iceland

108

Wearing which item of clothing during sex has been shown to increase a person's chance of having an orgasm?

a)   Hat
b)   Underwear
c)   Socks
d)   Shirt

109

A happy sex life has been linked with what?

a)   Improved job satisfaction
b)   Longer life
c)   Less incidence of heartburn
d)   Good eyesight

110
Which sex has reported higher incidences of low libido?

    a)   Men
    b)   Women
    c)   Both sexes are equal

111
Vibrators were originally invented to cure what medical issue in women?

    a)   Tuberculosis
    b)   Hysteria
    c)   Depression
    d)   Cancer

<u>112</u>

Citizens of which country have more sexual partners on average than any other country?

a) Austria
b) China
c) Morocco
d) Mexico

<u>113</u>

In 1969, which country legalized oral sex?

a) United States
b) Paraguay
c) Canada
d) Saudi Arabia

How well do you know your partner?

Where's my favorite place to have sex?

Sexy Prize: If your partner knows your favorite place to get it on, then orally pleasure them for two minutes anywhere they wish.

ROUND

10

114

Researchers have found that people with a strong sense of what have better, more frequent orgasms?

a) Touch
b) Taste
c) Smell
d) Hearing

115

The average sex session goes for how many thrusts?

a) 50-100 thrusts
b) 100-500 thrusts
c) 600-700 thrusts
d) 800-1000 thrusts

116
Research shows that women can make their voices sound sexier, but men cannot.

   a)   True
   b)   False

117
In the 1920s, young adults would have group parties filled with erotic exploration, kissing and fondling, but no sex. What were these get-togethers called?

a)   Petting parties
b)   Sexy soirées
c)   Innocent orgies
d)   Ice cream socials

118
Ancient Mayans liked to have sex in what?

a)   Rivers
b)   Temples
c)   Groups
d)   Hammocks

119

Which of these is the actual title of a medieval French poem?

a) The King and his lovely royal penis
b) The Knight who made cunts speak
c) The Queen loves dick more than tits
d) The Prince and the horny whore

120

Where was the cock ring invented?

a) China
b) Egpyt
c) Greece
d) Mexico

121
"Climacophilia" is sexual arousal at what?

a) Climbing a mountain
b) Falling down stairs
c) Watching others eat
d) Eating fruit

122
A 2005 study found which sex was sexually aroused by watching Chimpanzee porn?

a) Men
b) Women

123

Some women experience orgasms during childbirth?

    a)   True
    b)   False

124

What famous actress confessed to a friend that despite her many lovers, she never had an orgasm?

    a)   Audrey Hepburn
    b)   Elizabeth Taylor
    c)   Joan Crawford
    d)   Marilyn Monroe

How well do you know your partner?

What is one of my sexual fantasies?

Sexy Prize: If your partner can correctly name one of your sexual fantasies, then make one of their sexual fantasies come true right now.

What's it going to be?

Answers

Round 1
1. b) 66
2. b) 5 to 6 inches
3. d) All of the above
4. b) Women
5. a) 5.4 minutes
6. a) True
7. b) False
8. d) All of the above
9. a) True
10. b) 29%
11. b) False
12. c) 75%
13. d) 7.5

Round 2
14. b) False
15. b) False
16. a) 7
17. c) 25%
18. b) 10% - 15%
19. a) 8,000
20. a) True
21. c) 4,000
22. f) Greece
23. d) 1/8 inch per hour
24. c) Vasectomies
25. d) Fritz the Cat
26. a) 10%

Round 3

27. c) 28,000 years old
28. a) True
29. a) 94%
30. a) 64
31. c) Bites
32. a) True
33. b) 0.06%
34. b) Woman on top
35. b) To hide diseases like syphilis
36. b) False
37. a) True
38. d) All of the above

Round 4

39. c) A merging of the Victorian slang
40. a) Penguins
41. a) True
42. c) A threesome with two men and one woman
43. a) Snakeskin
44. a) True
45. b) 20-30%
46. b) It transmits information from the clitoris, scrotum, and penis
47. a) It's when two people get stuck together during sex
48. b) 30%
49. c) Unable to reach orgasm
50. b) His cholesterol
51. d) Jogging for 30 minutes

Round 5

52. d) On his prostate gland
53. c) Storms
54. c) 200 million
55. b) Dolly Parton
56. a) The hymen
57. c) Wisconsin
58. b) 58%
59. c) Nose
60. a) They were bisexual
61. b) Nevada
62. d) Feet
63. c) Car

Round 6

64. d) Chocolate
65. c) The Brown Bunny
66. c) 3rd Century
67. d) Woman on top
68. a) True
69. b) The little death
70. a) The difference in orgasm frequency between men and women
71. a) True
72. b) Guam
73. a) Left
74. c) Candle
75. b) False
76. d) 3%

Round 7

77. d) 71 minutes
78. c) Indonesia
79. b) 84%
80. d) Over 40 years old
81. a) Spain, Brazil, and Italy
82. b) Transgendered
83. b) False
84. c) Ferret
85. a) True
86. d) Alabama
87. a) Yes
88. b) 5-7 calories
89. c) 13.5 inches

Round 8

90. b) 15%
91. d) Crawling insects or worms
92. a) 919 men
93. b) Jason Momoa
94. a) Jennifer Aniston
95. c) Bats
96. d) Crocodile feces and sour milk
97. c) 30%
98. a) 17.4 years old
99. b) Sexual communication
100. a) True
101. b) Men

Round 9

102. b) Temporary amnesia
103. b) False
104. d) Bicycling
105. a) True
106. d) On an IKEA bed
107. b) Congo
108. c) Socks
109. a) Improved job satisfaction
110. c) Both sexes are equal
111. b) Hysteria
112. a) Austria
113. c) Canada

Round 10

114. c) Smell
115. b) 100-500 thrusts
116. a) True
117. a) Petting parties
118. d) Hammocks
119. b) The Knight who made cunts speak
120. a) China
121. b) Falling down stairs
122. b) Women
123. a) True
124. d) Marilyn Monroe

Spice up your love life even more, and explore all the discussion books for couples by J.R. James:

Love and Relationship Books for Couples

Would You Rather...? The Romantic Conversation Game for Couples (Love and Romance Edition)

Sexy Game Books for Couples

Would You Rather...? The Naughty Conversation Game for Couples (Hot and Sexy Edition)

Truth or Dare? The Sexy Game of Naughty Choices (Hot and Wild Edition)

Never Have I Ever... An Exciting and Sexy Game for Adults (Hot and Dirty Edition)

The Hot or Not Quiz for Couples: The Sexy Game of Naughty Questions and Revealing Answers

Pillow Talk: The Sexy Game of Naughty Trivia Questions for Couples

The Naughty Newlywed Game: A Sexy Game of Questions for Couples

Sexy Discussion Books for Couples

Let's Talk Sexy: Essential Conversation Starters to Explore Your Lover's Secret Desires and Transform Your Sex Life

All **THREE** *Let's Talk About...* sexy question books in one massive volume for one low price. Save now!

Let's Talk About... Sexual Fantasies and Desires: Questions and Conversation Starters for Couples Exploring Their Sexual Interests

Let's Talk About... Non-Monogamy: Questions and Conversation Starters for Couples Exploring Open Relationships, Swinging, or Polyamory

Let's Talk About... Kinks and Fetishes: Questions and Conversation Starters for Couples Exploring Their Sexual Wild Side

Change your sex life forever through the power of sexy fun with your spouse, partner, or lover!

www.sexygamesforcouples.com

Sexy Vacations for Couples
https://geni.us/Passion

ABOUT THE AUTHOR

J.R. James is a best-selling author who has a passion for bringing couples closer together and recharging their sexual intimacy. Erotic discussion is a powerfully sexy thing, and his conversation starter books have helped many couples reach new and sexually exciting heights in their relationships!

Sexy conversation with your partner is a magical, bonding experience. Through these best-selling question books, couples can find an easy way to engage in open and honest sexual discussion with each other. The result is a relationship that is both erotically charged and sexually liberating.

Made in the USA
Las Vegas, NV
14 December 2022